CONTENTS

ANATOMY OF FISHES

What is a fish? How does a codfish differ from a shark? Is a whale a fish? What about shellfishes, starfishes and jellyfishes? How many sorts of fishes are there? These are some of the often-asked questions that will be answered in this chapter.

To the scientists studying animals and finding out which animals are related to each other, and how closely they are related, the most important fact about all fishes is that they are vertebrate animals.

This means that they all possess a backbone made up of segments called vertebrae.

Many animals are called fishes just because they live in water—jellyfish, shellfish and starfish, for example. But none of these animals has a backbone. It can easily be seen that the transparent jellyfish does not have any bones. The next time that you eat any shellfish, cockles or winkles, for example, have a look for bones. You will not find any. Therefore, we can say that animals without backbones are not really fishes even if they are called a "something-fish".

Whales and porpoises are fish-like animals that have back-bones, fins, and live in the sea. Are they fishes? To many people's surprise, the answer is no. Whales and porpoises are mammals, not fishes. It is odd to find mammals that look like fishes, not like their close relatives, elephants, horses, cats, rabbits and humans, which are also mammals. Whales and porpoises (called Cetaceans) differ from fishes in several ways. Their bodies, like ours, stay at the same temperature regardless of how hot or cold it is in the water. The body of a fish is usually at the same temperature as the water. Whales breathe the oxygen in air, using lungs; fishes take the oxygen dissolved in water by means of their gills. Although whales have fin-like flippers, the bones supporting these fins are very similar to those in our arms. The fins of fishes are completely different in structure. Like all mammals, whales have young which are born fully developed and are fed on milk by their mothers. Most fish lay eggs.

4

The tails of whales are horizontal, the tails of fishes are vertical.

Killer whale—a mammal

Cod—a bony fish

So we can see from this that fishes are backboned animals that live in the water, and breathe by taking oxygen (the life-giving gas in air) dissolved in the water through their gills. They usually lay eggs, and have a body temperature which changes with the temperature of the water.

It is important to note here that many of the items listed

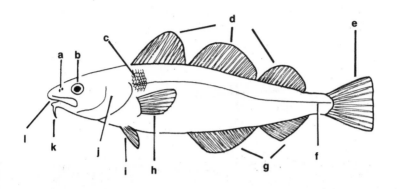

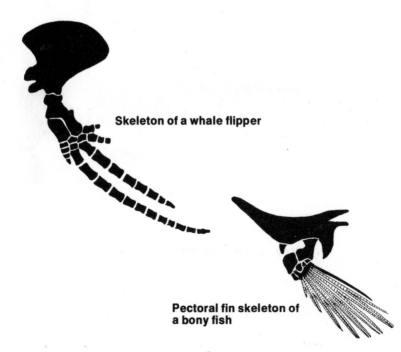

Skeleton of a whale flipper

Pectoral fin skeleton of a bony fish

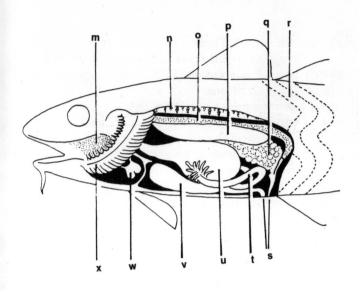

KEY TO PARTS OF FISHES

a, Nostril   b, Eye,   c, Scales   d, Dorsal fins

e, Caudal fin   f, Lateral line   g, Anal fins

h, Pectoral fin   i, Pelvic fin   j, Operculum

k, Barbel   l, Mouth   m, Oesophagus   n, Spine

o, Kidney   p, Swim bladder   q, Ovary

r, Muscles   s, Anus — Vent   t, Intestine

u, Stomach   v, Liver   w, Heart   x, Gills

7

above are generalizations. There are over 20,000 different types of fishes living under all sorts of conditions, and some have developed special adaptations which may make them exceptions to the generalizations.

Now that we have some idea of what a fish is, let us look at a fish in detail, examine its parts and find out what they are called. Look at the picture of the cod, a common food-fish living in the North Atlantic. The body is longer than it is deep, with a smooth outline so that it can slip easily through the water. One obvious feature of fishes is their fins. In a fish like the cod — a bony fish — these are made of thin, flexible rods of bone joined together by a thin membrane. The fins on the back are called dorsal fins. There are three of these in the cod. Some fishes have spines in their fins, other fishes have a small fleshy fin on their backs without any rays. This little fin is called the adipose fin. Adipose is a Greek word meaning fatty. The fin at the end of the body, the tail fin, or properly the caudal fin, is shaped differently in different species of fish. In some fish it is absent. On the underneath of the body near the caudal fin is the anal fin, and in front of that the paired fins are called the pelvic or ventral fins. The fins on a fish that are in the position of our arms are called the pectoral fins. Each fin has its own particular job to do in helping the fish to steer and brake when swimming. These functions will be described later.

Just in front of the eye, and above the mouth, is a small pit which is the fish's nostril. Behind the eye is a large, hinged plate of bone called the operculum or gill cover. This, as its name suggests, covers and protects the gills. It opens to let out the water which has passed through the gills and had the oxygen removed from it. The great majority of fishes have all the above characteristics.

Many of the internal organs of fishes do the same job as in ourselves, although they may be a lot simpler. The most easily recognizable organ that many fishes possess, and we don't, is the large, silvery swim bladder which lies along the top of the body cavity. This will be mentioned again later. Incidentally, the part of the fish that we eat — the flesh — is muscle.

TYPES OF FISHES

There are, as we have noted, over 20,000 different sorts of fishes. These are divided into three main groups, each of which is as different from the others as we are from birds or amphibians. Most are "fish-shaped", but this is what one would expect from animals that move swiftly through water.

These three groups are:

1. Cyclostomes or Agnathans (sy-klo-stomes or ag-nath-ans). These two words, both of which are used to describe these animals, mean "round-mouths" and "jawless". These are the most obvious characteristics of this class. The lampreys have no jaws, and their mouths are round. They have lips with tooth-like projections which they use to rasp away on soft materials, usually the flesh of dead fishes. There are only two species living now, which are the lampreys and hagfishes. There are more differences between this group and the others which, although not so conspicuous, are important to scientists. They

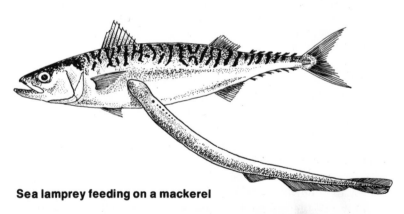

Sea lamprey feeding on a mackerel

include a series of gills connected by a long tube; a different type of spinal column called a notochord; no scales; no paired fins; and a much reduced and sunken "third eye" on the top of the head. This "third eye" is not as efficient as the other two, but can detect the difference between light and dark.

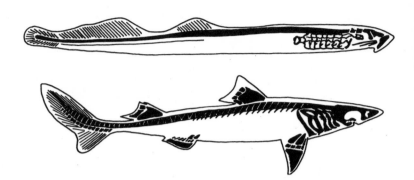

**Skeletons of a lamprey (above)
and a shark (below). Black
areas are cartilage**

2. Elasmobranchs (eel-as-mo-branks). This group contains
the sharks, skates and rays. These fishes have a skeleton made
of a gristle called cartilage (cart-il-aj), a series of, usually, five
gill-slits that can be seen on the outside of the fish, a skin
which has tiny tooth-like little plates called placoid (plakoid)
scales, and a skin which covers the fins so that the fin rays
cannot be seen. There is no bone in their skeleton, nor do they
have a swim bladder. Skates and rays (there is no difference
between the two – skate is a local name for some of the edible
rays) can be regarded as flattened sharks in which the pectoral
fins are very large and often called wings. All the other fins
are extremely small and the body behind the pelvic fins forms
the long, thin tail. Sharks have the gill-slits at the side of
the head, while rays have gill-slits on the underside. The sawfishes (which perhaps should really be called sawsharks) have
a body-shape between that of a shark and that of a ray. What
is interesting, though, is that there are two sorts: one that has
the gill-slits on the underside of the head and is therefore a
ray, and the other that has the gill-slits at the side of the head
and is therefore a shark. The saws are used to catch fish.

3. The other major group contains the fishes most familiar
to us, the bony fishes or Osteichthyes (ostay-ik-thees).

10

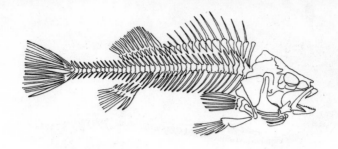

Skeleton of a bony fish

In this group, which has many more species than the other two groups, we find the cods, flying-fishes, angler-fishes, swordfishes, herrings, mackerel, blennies, and many more — in all about 20,000 different species. These fishes have a bony skeleton — only too well known if one eats an unfilleted kipper — gills which open into a single, large cavity protected by the gill cover — the operculum — fins which can be raised or lowered, and in which the fin rays can be seen, swim bladders, usually, and, frequently, scales. For particular reasons, certain fishes have lost some of these characteristics; some catfishes, for example, have no scales, while the trunkfishes have bodies rigidly enclosed in bony plates. The bodies of pipefishes are covered by a series of bony rings.

THE ORIGINS OF FISHES

Fishes have a very long history. They were the first vertebrates to appear in the world, about 400 million years ago in the Ordovician period. Not much is known about these very first fishes. All that remains of them are a few scattered pieces of bone preserved in rocks. We know that they were jawless fishes, like the lamprey, but with heavy, bony armour. Some of their descendants are found as beautifully preserved fossils in rocks of the Silurian and Devonian periods, about 350 to 275 million years ago. They had large, bony head-shields and

Overleaf. Sharks, rays and sawfish

11

looked very different from their living descendants. Luckily some were so perfectly preserved that their internal structure can be examined, and it has been found that they had the same important features as the living lampreys.

The first fishes with jaws appeared in the Upper Silurian. A little later – in the early Devonian – the ancestors of our living, bony fishes are first represented in the fossil record. The sharks were the last group to appear just before the middle of the Devonian period. Therefore, there has been about 300 million years of time in which to produce all the varied species living today. To put this into perspective, the first true men appeared less than half a million years ago.

As you can see from the picture, the earliest bony fishes and jawless fishes were clumsy-looking, heavily armoured species. During the course of their evolution they have lost much of this heavy armour and become more graceful. They are now much more mobile and more precisely adapted to their environment than their ancestors would seem to have been. For instance, in the earliest-known fishes we do not find all the different types alive today. There are no flatfishes, no eel-like fishes, no sunfishes, no flying-fishes; the general body-shape was a standard fish shape. Bearing that in mind, it is a little easier to see how, during the many millions of years that they have been living in the sea, different species have evolved which are adapted to live in a particular way.

SALT AND FRESH WATER FISHES

Almost all the cartilaginous fishes – sharks and rays – live in the sea. The exceptions include the Ganges shark and the Zambesi shark, both of which make long journeys up rivers, and some freshwater stingrays which are found in certain tropical rivers. The freshwater stingrays spend all their lives in fresh water and, therefore, breed there. Although

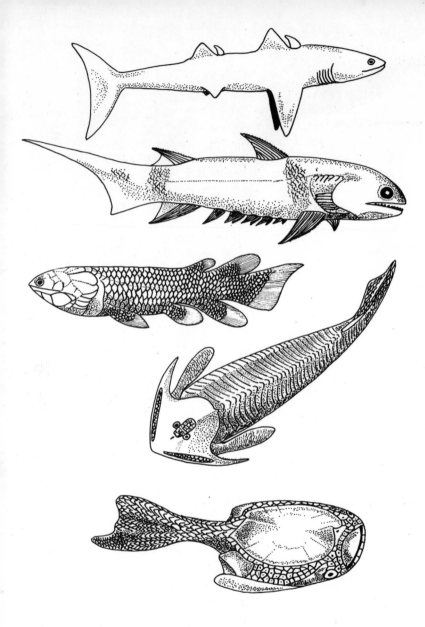

At the top is a primitive shark, followed by two early bony fishes and two early agnathans

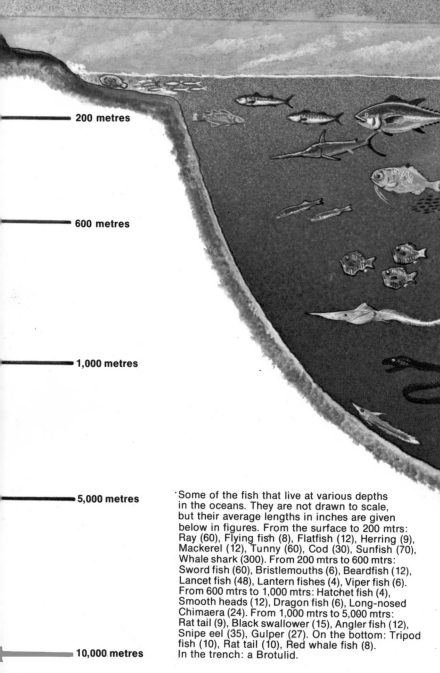

200 metres

600 metres

1,000 metres

5,000 metres

10,000 metres

Some of the fish that live at various depths in the oceans. They are not drawn to scale, but their average lengths in inches are given below in figures. From the surface to 200 mtrs: Ray (60), Flying fish (8), Flatfish (12), Herring (9), Mackerel (12), Tunny (60), Cod (30), Sunfish (70), Whale shark (300). From 200 mtrs to 600 mtrs: Sword fish (60), Bristlemouths (6), Beardfish (12), Lancet fish (48), Lantern fishes (4), Viper fish (6). From 600 mtrs to 1,000 mtrs: Hatchet fish (4), Smooth heads (12), Dragon fish (6), Long-nosed Chimaera (24). From 1,000 mtrs to 5,000 mtrs: Rat tail (9), Black swallower (15), Angler fish (12), Snipe eel (35), Gulper (27). On the bottom: Tripod fish (10), Rat tail (10), Red whale fish (8). In the trench: a Brotulid.

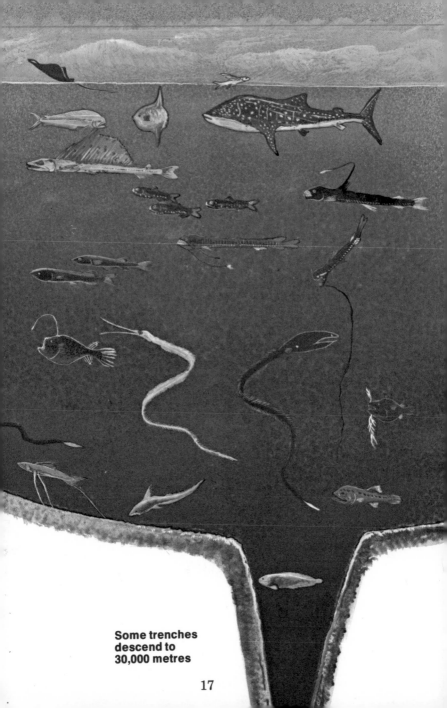

Some trenches descend to 30,000 metres

17

sharks are always present in the freshwater Lake Nicaragua, the population is continuously changing; those going back to the sea are replaced by individuals newly arrived from the the sea. The majority of bony fishes live in the sea. The several thousand species that live permanently in fresh water do not concern us here, but some species that are equally at home in the sea and in rivers and lakes will be mentioned. These include the eel, which spends most of its adult life in rivers and lakes but goes back to the sea to breed, and salmon which go to sea when adult to feed, but come back to fresh waters to breed.

Fishes that go down to the sea to breed, like the eel, are called catadromous (kat-ad-rome-us) fishes, while salmon and sturgeon that go into fresh water to breed are called anadromous (ann-ad-rome-us) fishes. Some fishes, like the flounder, spend their lives in river estuaries and are as happy in fresh

MAP OF DEPTHS IN THE OCEANS

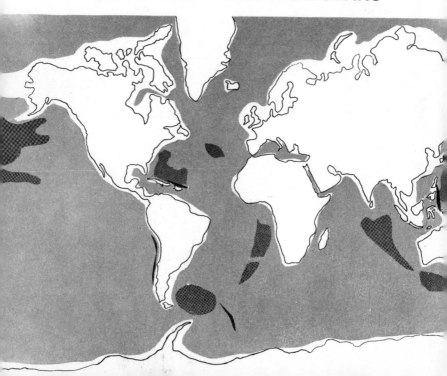

water as in salt water. An angler can catch a flounder in the sea as well as in a river.

HOW FISHES BREED

Fishes produce their young in a number of different ways. Adult fishes are usually tougher than their eggs or young, and can survive in conditions in which the young could not live. It is because of this that some species will migrate for hundreds of miles to lay their eggs in surroundings which give their young the best chance of survival.

Most bony fish lay eggs. In some, the eggs are just scattered into the water, in others they are laid in clumps. Some species make nests for young; some parents guard their young, while other parents will eat their own young and the young of any

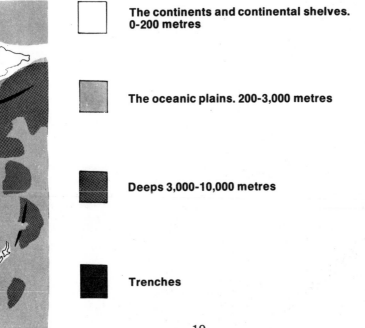

The continents and continental shelves. 0-200 metres

The oceanic plains. 200-3,000 metres

Deeps 3,000-10,000 metres

Trenches

other species that swims in front of them. The strange reproduction of the sea-horse, in which "the father has the babies", is another odd aspect of fish life which will be described later.

Some sharks and rays lay eggs which have leathery shells, while other sharks and rays (e.g. sting rays) give birth to fully formed young.

The lampreys spend up to seven years as blind larvae living in mud and feeding in a manner quite unlike that of their parents.

Some fishes form huge shoals, others lead solitary lives. Deep-sea fishes live in a cold world of permanent darkness where the next fish – and the next meal – may be a mile away. How do they find their food? How do they avoid becoming the food of another fish? Fishes that live in warm, tropical, shallow waters, especially in coral reefs, live very close together and are brightly coloured. How do they get enough food? Why are they brightly coloured when a herring is not?

Now that you have some idea of what fishes are, and how they come to be like this, we can try to answer some of the questions on how fishes live.

It is fitting that at the end of this introduction there should be a note of both apology and warning. The common skate, for example, is called skate in the south of England, roker in parts of the north of England. The French call it *pochete*, the Dutch, *vleet*, the Germans, *glattroche*, the Norwegians, *glatskate*. Similarly, to other English speakers, roker and skate are used for completely different fishes. With some species that are worldwide, calling a fish by a common name that everyone will understand is going to be impossible. Anyway, many fishes do not have any common names. The way that scientists overcome this is by a naming system which is universal. All scientists from all countries call the same species by its scientific name. These names are based on Latin or Greek and may be difficult to pronounce, but this is the only way to be sure that everybody knows which species is being talked about. The

Skate is *Raja batis* to all scientists, no matter what its common name is in different countries. A relative of this species that, among other common names, is called the long-nose skate is *Raja oxyrinchus* (rye-er oxy-rink-us). Where a convenient common name is available it will be used, but sometimes the scientific name will also be given, so that if you want to know more about that fish you can find it easily in textbooks and avoid confusion.

FISHES OF THE COASTAL WATERS

About seven-tenths of the surface of the earth is covered by the seas and oceans. If the bumps on the surface of the earth —the mountains—and the scratches on the floor of the sea— the ocean trenches—were smoothed out, the whole world would be covered by about 8,000 feet of water. As it is, the tallest mountain is just over 29,000 feet high, while the greatest ocean deeps are over 35,000 feet deep. The average depth of

A weaver fish, and a butterfish guarding its eggs

the sea is over 12,000 feet. This represents a lot of water, which in turn means a great deal of room in which fishes can live. The sea offers a multitude of different environments, from the cold waters lapping against the glaciers of Antarctica to the warm waters of a coral island; from the polluted estuaries and shorelines of industrial countries to the permanent, cold blackness of the deep ocean trenches. In all these environments, and in everything between, we find fishes, each species adapted to its own particular way of life.

In this chapter we shall look at examples of fishes from many different habitats, though all in shallow waters, mostly coastal.

You can see from the map that the shoreline, where the tides ebb and flow each day, is merely the edge of a shelf that surrounds the continents. This is called the continental shelf. The floor of the sea falls away sharply from the edge of the continental shelf to the deep sea. The floor of the deep sea is not flat and smooth everywhere, it has its mountains and valleys. Where some of these mountains rise out above the sea they are called islands.

Fish can live near the bottom of the sea, perhaps actually on the bottom, like flatfishes, or just near it and feeding from the bottom. Other fishes live in the surface waters or middle waters of the sea and never go near the bottom.

Firstly, we will look at some of the fishes that live on or near the bottom of the sea, from the shore to the edge of the continental shelf. In considering the food of these fishes, we must bear in mind one important fact — that plants need light in order to grow. Although the water from a tap looks clear, it actually absorbs light. Half the light that enters the sea near the shore has gone by the time it has passed through 6 feet of water. At one place off the coast of North America 99% of the light has disappeared at 26 feet down. In the Sargasso Sea, which is probably the clearest part of the ocean, 99% of the light has gone at 490 feet down. So, below this sort of depth, where no plants can grow, the fishes must feed on something else. But for the fishes of coastal waters, there is plant food, if that is what they need.

IN THE ROCK POOLS

When you go on holiday to the sea-side you may find rock pools – little pockets of water left behind in the rocks when the tide goes out. In these you can find some of the fishes that live near to the shore. At first you will see nothing, but if you wait quietly you may see fishes swim rapidly from one hideaway to another.

The fishes in a pool like this are faced with several problems in living. The sea is comparatively cool, yet on a hot day the small amount of water in a rock pool can become uncomfortably warm. On a rainy day the water may become less salty. In a small pool the fishes are more easily accessible to fish-eating birds. The last problem is overcome by the fishes being well camouflaged with mottled drab-browns and olive-greens to render them less conspicuous.

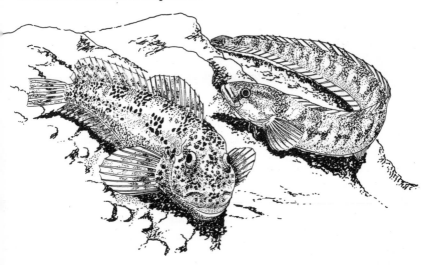

Shanny and viviparous blenny

The shanny (*Blennius pholis*) has no scales. It can grow to just over 6 inches in length, and is very common on rocky shores. It can change its colour to match its surroundings and, although usually greenish or brown, may become red if it lives in an area where there is a lot of red seaweed. The shanny can live for ten years, and although it has fang-like teeth at the front of its jaws, it will eat plants as readily as it will eat other fish. The butterfish (*Pholis gunnellus*, foe-lis gun-el-us) is another fish that spends a lot of time on the shore. If there are no rock pools it will wriggle under stones as the tide goes out and stay there until the tide comes back. It is a very slippery, slimy fish, hence its common name of butterfish. The breeding habits of this egg-laying species are interesting and are described later.

In contrast to this is another eel-shaped shore fish, the viviparous blenny. Despite its common name, this species is not a blenny, but it does give birth to fully formed young; the eggs hatch inside the mother. The young are about $1\frac{1}{2}$ inches long when born and the adult may reach 18 inches in length. This species is always found on the shores of north-west Europe and never in deep water, but it has some relatives that live only in deep water.

Many of the fishes that live on the shore are long and thin. This enables them to hide under stones, or in cracks in the rocks to keep moist when the tide goes out. Other fishes — young wrasses, for example — will, from time to time, be caught in rock pools. There are fewer shore fishes on sandy shores around our coasts, or at least they are more rarely found. If there is a lot of seaweed you may find pipefishes. In warmer waters, and very occasionally on the south coast of England, sea-horses have been found.

The cuckoo wrasse, the red band fish and the male dragonet

IN THE SHALLOWS

The shallow seas extend from below the low-tide mark to the edge of the continental shelf. There, most of our food-fishes are found. There are the flatfishes, like plaice and dabs, which, except for their larval period, hardly ever leave the bottom. There are haddock which feed largely off the bottom, cod which feed on the bottom, as well as in mid water, and the rocklings are also found on the bottom here, as well as in rock pools.

The cod and the haddock can easily be recognized by their three soft dorsal fins and their two anal fins. The haddock has a dark blotch above the pectoral fin, which is not present in cod. The cod is a mottled sandy-brown in colour, and the haddock a dark greeny-brown. Both these species — and almost all fishes — are paler on the underside than on the back. Not all the fishes of the waters of the continental shelves are edible or so dully coloured.

The weever-fishes live on sandy bottoms in shallow waters. There are two species around our coasts, the greater weever and the lesser weever. The latter species has a chunkier body, eyes on the top of its head, and an upturned mouth. Both are yellowish-brown in colour. There are two dorsal fins, a short, spiny one which has a black blotch and a longer, softer, pale-brown one. The black mark on the first dorsal fin is a danger sign, for it contains a poison spine. Another poison spine is found on the gill cover. These fishes, especially the lesser weever, lie in the sand in shallow water with only the top of the head and back sticking out. If anyone not wearing shoes treads on one of these fishes, the spines stab through the skin. The poison causes a very severe pain which may last for a day. This is most likely to happen to people when they are shrimping. Despite this, weevers are caught in small quantities commercially in Denmark and Germany, handled with care and used in making fish-meal. They eat shrimps and crabs. The lesser weever grows to 6 inches long and the greater weever, which lives in deeper water, to 16 inches long.

Most people associate brightly coloured fishes with coral reefs, but around our shores there are rivals to the coral-reef fishes. The dragonet, a slightly flattened fish, is very luridly coloured with blue and orange markings. The male dragonet has a much longer dorsal fin than the female. The cuckoo wrasse is also very brightly coloured, again in blues and oranges. One eel-like fish, which feeds on the bottom, is bright red in colour. This is the red band-fish which normally lives in the warmer waters of the Mediterranean, but is occasionally found round the southern shores of Great Britain. Hiding among rocks in this region, large conger eels can be found. In warmer waters their speckled relatives, the moray eels, lurk among the rocks ready to snap at any passing fish, or perhaps a diver who becomes too inquisitive for their liking. Their greeny-blotched bodies make them very difficult to see in their dappled world.

To some extent, similar fishes are found in the shallow waters of other parts of the world. However, there are many more round tropical shores than there are in polar seas.

IN THE CORAL REEFS

Tropical coral reefs form a wonderful shallow-water environment for fishes. There is plenty of food and many hiding places. Coral is not a plant, but is formed from the stony skeletons of great colonies of tiny animals called polyps (poll-ips) which are rather like miniature sea-anemones. They can form great reefs if the water is not too cold. Here you will find brilliantly coloured butterfly-fishes, some of which have long snouts, and delicately pick food out of the tiny cracks in the coral. Many butterfly-fishes have a dark spot near the tail which looks like another eye. This is supposed to mislead predators into biting the wrong end of the fish. Some of the coral-reef fishes have very different colour patterns at different stages of their lives; even the male and female may be so differently coloured that they have been mistaken for different species.

KEY TO CORAL REEF FISHES

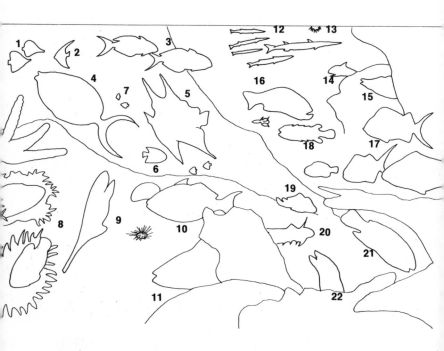

BY DAY

1. Beaked coral fish
2. Moorish idol
3. Golden trevally jacks
4. Unicorn fish
5. Cowfish
6. Banded humbug
7. Orange striped coral fish
8. Anemone fish (two species)
9. Longnose butterfly fish
10. Black-barred trigger fish
11. Spotted wrasse

BY NIGHT

12. Barracuda
13. Porcupine fish
14. Shark
15. Humpback "cod"
16. Grouper
17. White lined squirrel fish
18. Glass eye snapper
19. Stonefish
20. Flying Gurnard.
21. Parrot fish in "nightgown"
22. Moray eel

The surgeon-fish in tropical waters has a sharp blade of bone at either side of the base of its tail, which helps to protect it from predators. The boxfish has a rigid body made of bony plates. Only the tail and fins can move to help it swim. These fishes are brightly coloured, which is, in this case, a warning to would-be predators that their skin contains a poison. The boxfish can afford to move slowly in these waters since he is doubly protected by the bony plates and the poison. The puffer-fishes are also poisonous, but their main defence is to gulp air into their stomachs and blow themselves up like a ball. This not only helps to make them too big to eat, but it also makes their spine-like scales stand out on end. This may seem cunning, but it has its drawbacks. When they are inflated, they float upside down on the surface of the water, quite helpless. In this state they can be attacked by birds.

Swimming round mangrove swamps on tropical coastlines, you can find the beautiful batfishes. The young fishes, when they are alarmed, wrinkle up their large dorsal and anal fins, stop swimming, and sink slowly so that they look like dead leaves. The orange-and-cream anemone-fish lives among the stinging tentacles of sea-anemones. Many tropical sea-anemones feed on fishes, but the anemone-fish is either immune to their stings or in some way prevents the anemone from stinging. An anemone-fish separated from its anemone is usually soon eaten.

What is probably the most poisonous fish — and a strong candidate for the title of the most ugly — is the stonefish which inhabits these warm, tropical, coastal waters. It is a bulky fish which can change its colour to match its surroundings, and when fully camouflaged looks like a rock with assorted growths on it. It only rarely moves, relying on its camouflage to catch its unsuspecting prey. The spines on its dorsal fin carry a poison which can kill those humans unlucky enough to tread on one. Even the flesh is poisonous.

DAY AND NIGHT FISHES

One of the strange things about a coral reef is that the fishes occupy the cracks in the coral on a shift system. The little butterfly-fishes and others that are swimming round during the day seem to vanish at night, and their place is taken by large-eyed squirrel-fishes and soldier-fishes that have slept all day. Although most of the fishes sleep in cracks, one species, the rainbow parrot-fish, spins an envelope of slime round itself and sleeps in that. This can take about half an hour to complete. At first light, it takes the fish about the same length of time to free itself from this "bed". The parrot-fishes get their name from the beak-like form of their teeth. They have very strong jaws, and with their beaks break off and chew pieces of coral in order to eat the polyps.

IN THE POLAR SEAS

Very few fish species live round the cold polar shores, but some of these are most interesting. A group of fishes called Antarctic cods (although they are not related at all to the true cod) live round the ice-covered Antarctic. These fishes have large heads with large mouths, but most remarkable is the fact that their blood is colourless. All other fishes have red blood in which the red pigment, haemoglobin (heem-o-globe-in) in the corpuscles carries the oxygen. The Antarctic cods—also called ice fishes—are not very active and can manage to live on the oxygen simply dissolved in the blood plasma.

**Antarctic cod
or ice fish**

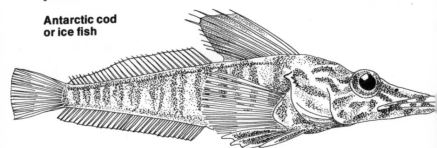

Another bizarre fish of tropical shallow waters is the little glassfish (*Chanda ranga*). This fish is so transparent that its bones can be seen. The stomach and some of the internal organs are hidden inside a silvery bag, but the rest of the fish is so clear that you can see right through it. The glassfish can live in fresh water, and is often kept by aquarists. In parts of India it is so common that shoals are caught and used as fertilizer.

Most of the catfishes live in fresh waters, but there is one group, the ariids, also called crucifix-fish that live in the shallow, tropical seas. These fishes have the odd habit of incubating eggs in their mouths. This job is usually done by the male which swims round with a mouthful of eggs — and each egg is nearly as big as a marble — until they hatch. The name crucifix comes from the shape of the bones on the underside of the skull. The shape resembles a man on a cross, and is used by some natives as a religious ornament.

So far we have not mentioned any of the sharks. Naturally enough, wherever there are a lot of fish to eat, you will find sharks, so that there are plenty in the rich, tropical shallows. However, as many sharks spend their time in the deeper open waters, they will be discussed, along with the deep-sea fishes, in the next chapter.

We have had time for only a brief look at just a few of the many species that live in the coastal waters and shallow seas. Some fishes that live here, like the electric-fishes and the sea-horses, will be described in detail in later chapters. But before we leave this coastal region, I want to mention one particular fish, the archer, and a fascinating group of unrelated fishes that all have the same strange habits. The archer-fish lives round the shores and estuaries of the Pacific Ocean. It is not a very large nor a very beautiful fish, but it is remarkable for its ability to spit out drops of water with which it can hit a fly on a leaf a few feet away. The archer-fish gets much of its food in this way. It has a groove in its mouth, and when shooting, it presses its tongue into the groove to form a narrow "rifle barrel" and then it squirts the water out. At

Archer fish

a distance of 3 feet, it usually hits the insect first time. Naturally, these fishes are found where there are plants overhanging the water.

CLEANER FISH

The group of fishes that I have chosen to close this chapter with are the cleaner-fishes. These come mostly from two families, the wrasses and the gobies. They have pointed snouts with tweezer-like teeth at the end, are very brightly coloured, and each fish always lives in the same place. When another fish has any parasites on its skin it visits the area where the cleaner-fish lives, and waits for the cleaner to come out and nibble off the parasites. Large fishes will even let the little cleaners into their mouths and gills to eat the parasites. While doing its job, the cleaner is not eaten. The cleaner-fish does not perform this service out of the kindness of its heart, for it

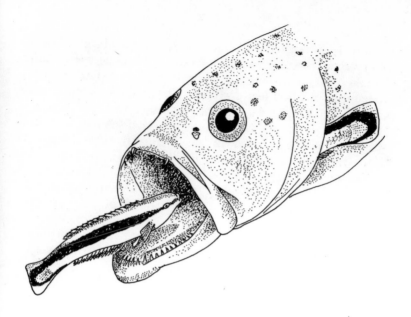

Cleaner fish at work on a grouper

eats the parasites. This arrangement, as you will see later, is only one of many remarkable examples of fish behaviour.

FISHES OF THE OPEN SEAS

The fishes described in a previous section live just round the edges of the oceans. The floor of the ocean drops away sharply at the edge of the fish-rich continental shelf, down to regions of cold and lightless water. There is little plant food available and for many of the fishes of the deeper waters the rule is eat or be eaten. High above in the sunlit, surface waters there are many more fishes, but these are fishes that may never see a shoreline nor the bottom of the sea. They must spend all their life buoyed up by water, for if the sea-floor is 30,000 feet below them, they can hardly rest on the bottom. It is with the fishes of the open ocean and its depths that we are concerned with in this section.

There is never a hard and fast line separating shallow-water fishes from deep-water fishes, nor a line between shore fish and open-ocean fish. A trawler fishing for cod at night in water perhaps 1,500 feet down is quite likely to catch, along with the cod, strange fishes with very large eyes and glowing patches of light on the body. These are deep-sea fishes at the upper end of their depth range. Naturally, there are no shallow-water fishes at greater depths, but there is always an area of overlap where the shallow-water, deep-sea and open-ocean fishes are found together. Some sorts of fishes, especially open-ocean fishes, may be found in each of the three areas.

We will consider, firstly, the fishes found in the surface waters of the oceans far from land. Some of them are very large, and others are small.

TYPICAL SHARKS

The largest of all fishes, the whale-shark, grows to over 40 feet long. It spends most of its time cruising slowly around the warm, surface waters of the tropical oceans. All the while it swims it feeds. Unlike most other sharks which are carnivorous, the whale-shark feeds on the very small sea animals (crustaceans, small fishes and fishes at their larval stages, collectively called plankton), which it strains from the water flowing into its mouth and out through its gills. The whale-shark, apart from its size, is quite unmistakable with its white-spotted body. Not a great deal is known about this fish and, in fact, it seems to be quite rare.

More typical sharks cruise round the surface waters of the tropics and temperate regions. They are usually grey or blue in colour, and the sight of the triangular dorsal fin cleaving through the waves is well known.

The majority of sharks are carnivores and will eat anything from man to fish. Sharks have several rows of pointed or cutting, triangular teeth which are constantly being replaced so that sharp, new teeth are always ready for action. The teeth point backwards to prevent the escape of the prey. The eyesight of sharks is said to be poor, so they must find their food by smell. This explains how, when one shark has bitten its prey and released blood into the water, other sharks pick up the scent of blood and follow it. Normally sharks do not eat humans. Fishes are their usual diet, but sometimes, perhaps

Thresher shark with remoras

several times a year throughout the world, bathers are attacked by sharks. It is not known why sharks should come so close inshore. In fact, not very much is known about shark attacks on humans. Recent surveys have shown that most shark attacks occur in the afternoon, and mostly in the southern hemisphere in summer. But this period is when more people are in the water. Most attacks occur within 100 feet of the shore, again where there are most people. About fifteen of the larger species of sharks are known to have been involved in attacks on humans.

The typical shark has a powerful streamlined body, crescent-shaped fins, and a very rough skin. The skin is covered with small, bony plates, called placoid scales or denticles, which are smooth when rubbed from head to tail, but rasping when rubbed the other way. Dogfishes are small sharks and are shaped like their larger relatives. A few sharks are different in shape. The thresher-shark has a very long upper lobe to its tail fin; it is supposed to thrash this in the water to herd together small fishes before eating them. The hammer-head shark, which grows to 20 feet in length, has a flattened head, with its eyes

Hammerhead shark

at the ends of projections. This shark, like most others, has its mouth on the underside of its head, and while it is largely a scavenger, it has been known to attack man.

Although sharks have a reputation for being dangerous and ferocious they are not particularly intelligent animals. Not all sharks are large. There are some luminous deep-sea sharks which never grow to more than a foot long. The largest sharks, like the largest rays, are plankton feeders.

From a fish's point of view, the bluefish (*Pomatomus*) is very much more savage than any shark. This stocky fish lives in the tropical and temperate waters of the Atlantic and may grow to over 4 feet long. It swims near the surface in shoals, and in general shape looks rather like a tunny. This fish has been described as "an animated chopping machine". The shoals of bluefishes pursue shoals of smaller fishes—often herring-like fishes—and bite any that come within range of their jaws. If the prey is too large to swallow, the hind part is bitten off and the rest left to sink. When a shoal of bluefishes are feeding, the sea is blood-stained and littered with pieces of fish. Sometimes shoals of bluefishes will drive their prey onto a beach, where they may be seen piled up in heaps as they have tried to escape from the hunters. The bluefish and its prey provide a wonderful example of how rich the sea can be. It has been estimated that about a thousand million bluefishes are in the western Atlantic waters each summer. A bluefish will eat ten fish per day and the summer bluefish season lasts about 120 days. This gives the staggering result that the adult bluefish population consumes 1,200,000,000,000 other fishes in less than half a year. Despite this, the stocks of both the prey and the predator remain constant.

Not all surface-water fishes behave like sharks or bluefish. The sunfish (*Mola mola*) is almost round when looked at from the side, although very thin when looked at from the front. It can grow to a ton in weight. It has a very small mouth with beak-like teeth and can only eat small fishes. It has almost no tail fin and swims—mostly on its side—by rowing movements of its oar-like dorsal and anal fins. The sunfish has no scales, but its skin is so thick and leathery, with a thick layer of gristle below it, that despite its lack of mobility it is in no great danger from enemies. The body of the sunfish is a grey-brown in colour, quite dull when compared to the similarly shaped opah (*Lampris regius*). This fish, like the sunfish, has a worldwide distribution in the open oceans. Although the opah looks as if it can only swim slowly, it feeds largely on squids, so it must be able to move fast enough to catch them.

FISH OF MANY SHAPES

Sharks have streamlined bodies, sunfishes and opahs have deep, rounded bodies while the scabbard-fishes and dealfishes have ribbon-like bodies. Despite the problems of a life involving continual swimming, the body-shape of the fish of the open ocean is very variable. The dealfish is a relative of the opah. It has a ribbon-like body, and grows to $8\frac{1}{2}$ feet long. The body is brilliantly silver, with a long, red dorsal fin. In the adult fish, only the upper lobe of the tail fin is present. This is bright-red and sticks out at a right angle from the end of the body, immediately behind the dorsal fin. This species lives in the upper waters and eats small fishes, squids, and jellyfishes.

Flying-fishes, which look a little like herrings with large fins, are surface-living fishes. Their flight will be described in detail in a later section.

Bluefish

Not all the oceanic fish are large. The skipper, a relative of the flying-fish, is rarely more than 1 foot long. It lives in shoals in the warmer parts of the Atlantic. The long jaws are used to feed on small fishes and crustaceans. The fins of the skipper are small but it gets its name from frequently leaping out of the water, a habit which its relative, the flying-fish, has taken much further.

Among the plankton floating in the surface waters are many fish eggs and larval fishes. Here there is plenty of small food particles and the young fishes can feed and grow before, in some cases, descending to the deeper waters which are poor in food.

COLOURING AND DEPTH

Most of the fishes in the light regions are silvery or brightly coloured. Fishes from the dark, deeper waters have either lost their colour or are velvety-black or brown. Many have luminous spots along the sides of their bodies.

The deep-sea lantern-fishes are often found near the surface at night. Each day, as the sun sets, shoals of these little fishes start to swim several hundred yards towards the surface. These little fishes are only a few inches long, so for them it is a long journey. They go to the surface to feed on the plankton. Before the sun rises they have started their descent down to the dark

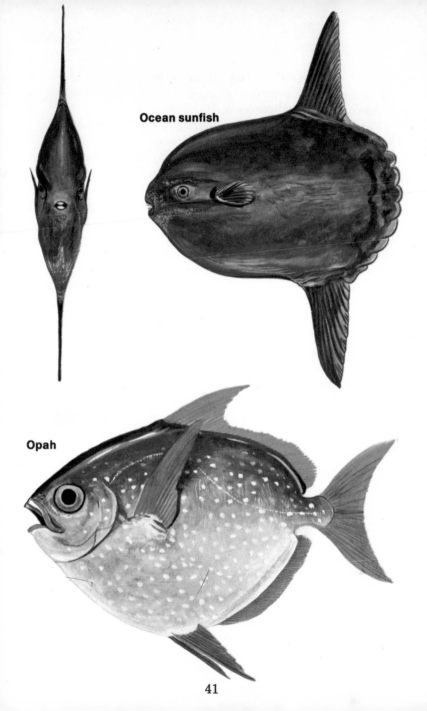

Ocean sunfish

Opah

41

waters. Lantern-fishes, and the other deep-sea fishes, live off the edge of the continental shelf, but strong currents may occasionally wash them towards the shore.

Because there is no light, there are no plants in the deep sea. The water is cold, even at the equator, so that the growth of the fishes is slow. Therefore, most of the deep-sea fishes, although ugly and perhaps frightening to look at, are quite small.

Hatchet-fishes are among the commonest of the deep-sea fishes. They have silvery-black bodies, big eyes and large, luminous organs. The mechanisms that make these luminous patches work will be described in a later chapter. Lantern-fishes and deep-sea hatchet-fishes have their luminous organs arranged in precise patterns, which help the fishes to recognize each other.

Rat-tails or grenadiers are relatives of the cod, and they have a luminous patch of slime just in front of the anal fin. Rat-tails, as their name suggests, have long tapering bodies. They live on the bottom and will eat any small invertebrates stirred up by their pointed snouts.

FISHES THAT FISH

A most remarkable use of light is shown by the deep-sea angler-fishes. The common angler-fish (*Lophius piscatorius*) of shallow seas is flattened from top to bottom, has a large mouth and lives on the bottom. The name angler-fish comes from the fact that the first ray of the dorsal fin is very long and has a small flap at the end. This overhangs the mouth and is waved about to tempt little fish to bite it. When they approach, the angler-fish surges forward and swallows them. The deep-sea angler-fishes are much smaller than *Lophius piscatorius* and do not live on the bottom. They have fragile, round bodies, very large mouths and large, needle-like teeth. The bait on their fishing-rod—the first dorsal fin ray—is luminous. Some species can move this fishing-rod back very slowly to draw the prey nearer to their mouths. Other species have a series of

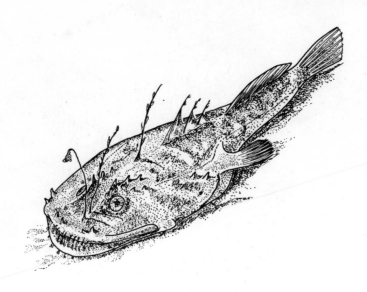

Common angler-fish

branching flaps below their chins, but the purpose of these is not known. The bait can shine with a flickering yellow-green, blue-green or orange-purple light, which must be very tempting to the animals in this black region.

The ultimate in catching prey is shown in an angler-fish called "*Galatheathauma*" (gal-at-ear-thow-ma) which has a luminous flap at the back of its throat. This fish simply lies with its mouth open and waits for an inquisitive fish to swim inside.

Overleaf on page 44. Fishes of the mid depths. A loose-jaw chasing a lantern fish. A hatchet fish. A long barbeled stomiatoid. An angler-fish. A snipe eel (pink). A guiper eel (black)

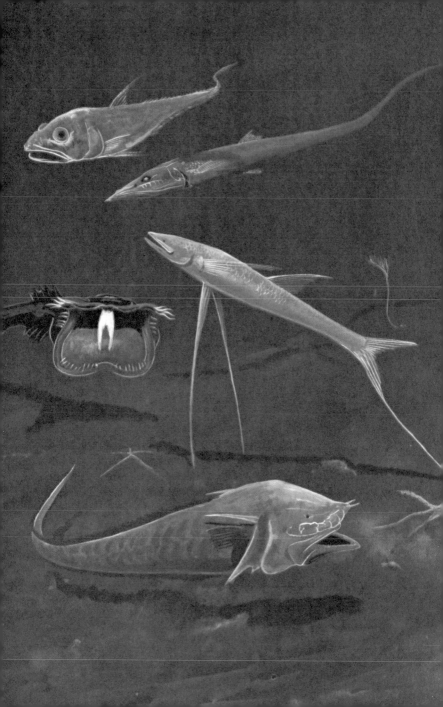

DEEP-SEA EELS

Eels are well represented in the deep sea. Snipe eels have long, thin jaws, covered with very tiny teeth. The jaws curve away from each other, like the sides of a trumpet. Recent observations have shown that these unlikely jaws are used to catch the long-legged, deep-sea shrimps and their relatives. Because food is hard to find in the deep sea, some fishes have elastic stomachs which enable them to swallow prey larger than themselves. The deep-sea gulper eels have, when hungry, a thin, tapering body with a cavernous elastic-sided mouth. The brain is minute — the fish is just a large mouth with a food receptacle behind it. When the gulper eel has swallowed another fish, the shape of the prey can be clearly seen through the distended body wall.

A fish called *Chauliodus* (call-e-ode-us) has a special adaptation that enables it to swallow large prey. The lower jaw can be pulled right down and then the head is jerked back to increase the size of the mouth. A relative of *Chauliodus*, called *Malacosteus*, has lost the sides and floor of the mouth, so that nothing hinders it opening its jaws. The jaws have long, needle-like teeth, and without the sides and floor of the mouth they can be thrust forwards with great speed and then snapped back, catching the prey. Small prey can escape through the openings, but the large prey have little chance.

Some deep-sea fishes have large eyes in order to see in what

Overleaf on page 45. Fishes of the ocean floor. Two rat-tails. Galatheathauma. A tripod fish. A brotulid little light there is. Others have no eyes at all. A fish called *Opisthoproctus* (o-piss-tho-proct-us) has telescopic eyes which point upwards. They cannot be moved to look forwards. The larvae of a fish called *Idiacanthus* (id-ee-ak-anth-us) have eyes mounted at the end of long stalks. As the fish grows, the stalks shrink, so that when the fish is adult the eyes are in a normal position. Many years ago an expedition to the Antarctic saw a deep-sea fish swimming at the surface. It had luminous organs behind the eyes and these acted like headlights of a car. The light-beams enabled the fish to see the small crustaceans on which it fed.

Fishes without eyes use their lateral-line system; this is very sensitive in detecting vibrations which warn of the approach of prey or predator.

Little is known about the breeding habits of deep-sea fishes, but the little that is known is remarkable. One of the problems for deep-sea fishes is finding a partner at the right time of year. The angler-fishes have overcome this problem in a remarkable way. The males are very small, and when they meet a female they bite on her body and eventually completely fuse, sharing her blood system. This will be discussed in detail in a later chapter.

Deep-sea fishes present many problems. Their adaptations are as extraordinary as is their mode of life. Some groups originated in the deep sea, others developed from surface- or shore-dwelling forms. One group of blind, deep-sea fishes — the brotulids — are confined to the deep sea except for two species found in freshwater caves in Cuba. It is very difficult to study deep-sea fishes because they are so fragile that they are damaged by the time they are brought to the surface. Deep-sea submarines, which have penetrated to the bottom of the deepest trenches, now enable scientists to see some of these strange fishes alive and feeding.

Different ways in which fish swim. The shark
uses its pectoral fins. The trigger fish swims
by undulating its dorsal and anal fins. The eel
undulates its whole body. The cod undulates the
rear half of its body. The tunny uses the tail

Different body shapes in fishes. The degree of streamlining is not always apparent in a side view, but generally speaking the fastest swimming fishes have the most obviously streamlined bodies

THE MOVEMENT OF FISHES

We live surrounded by air. Most of the time we don't think about it at all since it does not occur to us that air could be difficult to live in. However, have you noticed that walking against a strong wind is hard work? You can feel the resistance, you can feel the wind making it difficult to walk. Wind is only air moving.

Water is over 700 times denser than air. For humans, it is much easier to walk than to swim. On the other hand, we can float in water but not in air. How, then, do fish manage to live in this strange environment?

How do fishes swim? How do fishes see under water? Do they communicate with each other? What senses do fishes have? Do fishes sleep? Do they have hearts and brains? What makes the luminous, deep-sea fish luminous? How do electric-fishes get their electricity? These are some of the questions that we will try to answer in this chapter.

To start with, most fishes are about as dense as water; this means that they can float with very little effort.

The one fact about fishes that most people know is that they swim. Swimming is made much easier if the fish does not have to work hard in keeping afloat. Therefore, fishes have various ways of ensuring that their bodies are about the same density as the water in which they are swimming. Many bony fishes use the gas in their swim bladders to keep buoyant; this acts as air-filled water-wings do when small children learn to swim.

Those of you who swim will know that pressure increases with depth. Any fish making a journey from deep water into shallow water is presented with the problem of the gas in the swim bladder expanding as the pressure becomes less. The reverse problem occurs when a fish goes from shallow water into deep water. In most sea fishes there are many blood vessels in the swim-bladder wall, forming a gas gland. This gland secretes gas into the swim bladder as the fish goes deeper, thereby keeping the pressure constant. When the fish ascends, the gas gland absorbs air, preventing the swim bladder from enlarging. Naturally this is not a very rapid process, as can be seen when fish are trawled up by fishermen. A netful of cod, for example, caught in only a few hundred feet of water have their swim bladders so distended by the time they have been hoisted up to the surface that the expanded swim bladder sticks out of the mouth.

Some bony fishes, like the common angler-fish and the flat-fishes, live on the bottom of the sea. They have no need of a swim bladder to keep them afloat, and in these fishes the swim bladder is absent. These fishes are clumsy swimmers, not only because of their less streamlined shape, but also because some of their swimming effort is used in keeping afloat.

Tunny are large relatives of the mackerel and spend their lives swimming swiftly in the warmer, surface waters of the ocean. Despite this, they have lost their swim bladders. They maintain their buoyancy by having a lot of oil and fats in the flesh. The oil is lighter than water and helps them stay afloat. Tunny are also excellent, efficient swimmers, with very muscular bodies, and do not find themselves troubled by any buoyancy problems.

None of the sharks or rays has a swim bladder. One of the effects of this is that they do not find it difficult to swim up quickly from a great depth. To some extent, the level at which a shark swims is controlled by its speed of swimming. The angle at which the pectoral fins join the body is such that there is a hydroplane effect which pushes the front end of the body upwards as it swims faster. When swimming at maximum speed, the dorsal fin of the shark may stick out of the water. To explain this fully needs a detailed description of the way in which a fish swims, and as there is a basic similarity in the swimming movements of most fishes, we will study a shark to demonstrate this point.

Firstly, most of the power for pushing a fish through the water comes from the muscles of the flanks contracting on each side of the body in turn. In other words, the body wags from side to side. The wag is widest at the tail and it is this movement which pushes the fish forwards. The other fins may also be used, but to a lesser degree. As the tail fin follows the curve caused by the body wagging from side to side, part of the force produced by the muscles is changed into a thrust which pushes the body forwards. All this sounds rather complicated, and regrettably it is. The sideways wagging of the body is a shortened version of the curves into which a long body, like that of an eel (or even a snake moving on a smooth surface), is thrown. The diagrams illustrate what happens.

A shark has very little movement in its pectoral fins. These act like keels, set, as we noted above, at an angle to the body in such a way that any forward movement of the fish lifts the front part of the body. If this were carried to extremes, when travelling very fast the front part of the body would be forced up so far that the fish could not swim forwards at all. To counteract this, the shark has a tail in which the upper lobe is longer than the lower lobe. This has the effect of forcing the head down again. By careful adjustment of its speed, the shark can stabilize the level at which it swims. To rise up, it will generally swim faster.

We know that most of the thrust for swimming comes from the tail. Therefore, by looking at the tail and shape of the rear end of the body of the fish, we should be able to get some idea of whether the fish is a fast swimmer or not. The tunny is a fish which swims very quickly. The part of the body just before the tail fin — the caudal peduncle — is narrow; this offers less resistance to the water. The tail fin is high and crescent-shaped and remains rigid against the resistance of the water. As a general

Poisonous and electric fishes. From the top. A sting ray. Lion fish (Pterois). Stone fish. Electric ray. Puffer fish

rule, fishes with a tail fin like the tunny — that is, a lunate fin — are capable of swimming swiftly for long periods. Their bodies are well streamlined, and the gap between the lobes of the tail minimizes the drag effect caused by the turbulence of the body going through water.

A fish with a square-cut tail fin (for example, a haddock) cannot swim very quickly because the body-shape and soft, square-cut tail fin offer too much resistance to the water. However, fishes with a large tail and the dorsal and anal fins far back on the body can usually accelerate very rapidly to catch their prey. If we look at a long-bodied fish — an eel — a medium-bodied fish — a tunny — and a short-bodied fish — a trigger-fish — we can see how each has adopted its own method of moving.

An eel has no separate tail fin; when swimming, its body is thrown into several complete curves. The body of the tunny forms just about one curve, and there is a large tail fin. The body of the trigger-fish is short and deep, its body bends very little and, in this case, the movement of the fins is of great help in swimming. The trigger-fish cruises very slowly, using the waves passing along its dorsal and anal fins to supplement the power provided by the body. The sea-horse swims by rapidly vibrating its dorsal fin. It has no tail fin, but instead the rear end of its body is prehensile, and can curl round seaweed to anchor it. For most fishes, the other fins are not used in swimming; they work as stabilizers and help to balance and steer the fish. When fishes like the swordfish and tunny are swimming very fast, all the fins, except the tail fin, are folded back into grooves or depressions in the body to increase the streamlined shape of the body.

Fins may be put to very specialized uses. The first few rays of the dorsal fin of the angler-fish are used to lure its prey. The remora, or shark sucker, has a sucking disc on the top of its head. This disc is formed from its dorsal fin. The female ghost pipefishes have their egg pouch formed from the pelvic fins. The lumpsucker, or sea-hen, has a sucking disc on its belly formed from the pelvic fins.

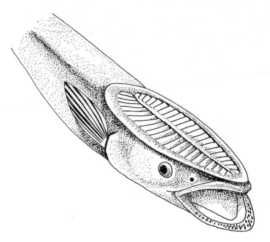

The head of a remora.
The sucker is formed
from the fin rays of
the first dorsal fin

POISON SPINES

The fins of bony fishes are made up from a series of movable bony rays, usually joined together by a membrane. Some of the fin rays may be thickened to form strong spines which can deter a would-be predator. The stonefish, for example, has developed poison glands. These lie beneath the skin at the base of the dorsal-fin spines. The spines have ducts which can carry the poison from the gland into the wound caused by the spine. If one of these fishes is handled carelessly, and enough pressure is put on the spine to make it penetrate the skin of the fisherman, the poison is released. Because of the pressure, it is injected into the wound, rather like the action of a hypodermic syringe.

The stingray has a spine at the base of its tail that contains a dangerous poison. Poison glands and spines may be found in the pectoral fin of some sea catfishes and on the gill cover of the weever-fish.

COLOUR PATTERNS

Often the fishes that have poisonous flesh are brightly coloured to warn other fishes of the danger in eating them. Because in many cases the colour pattern of bony fishes is the same in all members of the same species, fishes must be able to see in colour, since this is the way they recognize their own kind. Sharks and rays, which are drably coloured, probably do not have colour vision. Some coral-reef fishes are brilliantly coloured with spots and whorls. This has, on some occasions, confused scientists. For example, there are a few species in which the males and females have completely different colour patterns. These had been described as different species until it was realized that one species had only males in it and another only females.

The Atlantic bluehead wrasse has different colour patterns at different stages in its life. Flatfishes are particularly adept at changing their colour so that they match the sea-bed and stay well camouflaged.

In the fish's skin there are cells containing black, yellow, red or orange pigment. These cells can expand or contract, darkening or lightening each of these colours; there are also many silvery granules. The colours are produced by the way the fish organizes the cells and granules, and the effect that the light has on the combinations of colours. A green colour, for example, can be produced by a combination of a particular density of black and yellow pigments.

SLEEP IN FISHES

In the dark, the colour of fishes usually pales, so that, when sleeping, fishes are lighter in colour than when they are awake. Not very much is known about sleep in fishes, but cer-

**Above, the colour pattern in
a bluehead wrasse at different
stages in its life**

**Below, a flatfish pictured
against different backgrounds**

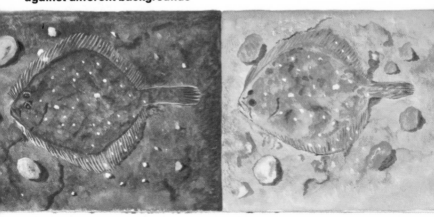

tainly most fishes do sleep. The sharks, for example, rest on the bottom to sleep because they cannot stay afloat without swimming.

Some coral-reef fishes lie on their sides on the bottom to sleep. One species of parrot-fishes spends up to half an hour secreting a coat of mucus round itself. It sleeps in this, and then when the sun rises spends the same length of time "getting out of bed". Another fish with an odd sleeping habit is a sole which passes the day on the bottom, but has been reported floating at the surface of the water asleep. Some fishes, especially open-ocean fishes, probably sleep in a series of short "cat-naps" throughout the day and night.

The drawings of the coral reef show that different fishes are awake during the day and during the night.

LIGHT IN FISHES

As the sun goes down, a large number of deep-sea fishes begin to swim towards the surface to feed upon the small animals — plankton — found there. Some fishes travel more than 1,000 feet up and down each day. This not only involves great changes of pressure, it also means that they may come from moderately cold water into warm water. The temperature difference may be as much as 25°F. Among the commonest fishes undergoing this daily migration are the little lantern fishes. They are small, rarely more than 6 inches long and get their name from the luminous spots on their body. Luminosity is quite common in mid-water fishes.

Several suggestions have been put forward to explain the function of light organs in lantern fishes. One suggestion is that as each species of fish has a pattern of light organs peculiar to itself members of the same species can recognize each other. This enables them to form shoals and to find their mates in the breeding season. Another suggestion advocates that the light organs may act as camouflage to break up the outline of the fish and to render it less conspicuous against a lighter background. One scientist noticed that most of the lantern fishes taken from the stomachs of deep sea predators were males. The males have brighter luminous organs than the females and it may be, he argued, that the males deliberately sacrifice themselves to protect the females. The species can survive with a reduced number of males but not with a reduced number of females.

Some lantern fishes and some fishes of another group of deep sea inhabitants — the stomiatoids — have light organs arranged in such a way that they may well use them to light up the surrounding waters to see their prey.

Light is produced in two ways. Some fishes, like the angler fish, use colonies of luminous bacteria contained in cells as the light source. Others, like many stomiatoids, emit light from glands in which a chemical reaction, under the control of the fish, produces the light. Once the light is produced it can be filtered, focused or shut off by ingenious arrangements of coloured, lens-like or opaque shields often produced from scales. Most of the light produced is blue or green but lilac, red, yellow and orange lights have been recorded.

Generally light organs point downwards. Why, is not known, but it may be concerned with the camouflage problem mentioned above.

The light is not always confined to particular organs. Some deep sea sharks have a faint luminous glow over most of the body. The Rat-tails (deep sea relatives of the cod) produce a luminous shine from a gland by the anus. Some angler fishes have faintly luminous teeth — one would think that this would be a disadvantage to a fish relying on a luminous lure to attract its prey.

There is a surprising amount of animal light in some regions of the sea. Not only do the fishes twinkle but also the shrimps, jellyfishes, squids and worms. Even the Bombay duck (actually a fish from the shallow waters of the Indian Ocean) has luminous organs!

The pattern of light along the side of each fish is the same in all members of the same species, and helps them to recognize one another. Generally the light comes from two sources, either special glands containing luminous bacteria, or glands in which a light-producing chemical reaction is going on. The glands are called photophores. They are usually cup-shaped and may also have focusing lenses, blinds or coloured filters. In this way the fish can control the amount, and often the colour, of the light produced.

ELECTRIC FISHES

As well as producing light, some fishes can also produce electricity. This has been studied much more in some freshwater fishes like the electric-eel (which is not an eel) and the electric catfish than in sea fish. It is known that the former fish uses the electricity both for stunning its prey and for a sort of radar or echo-location. The electric-ray, or torpedo, is a flat, rounded ray found in warm waters, and its numbing properties were known to the ancient Greeks.

Every time you move a muscle, a minute amount of electricity is involved in stimulating the muscle fibre to contract. The electric organs of fishes are derived from muscle fibres which no longer contract, but have the power to store up electricity and release it when needed. One species of electric-ray (*Torpedo nobiliana*) grows up to 6 feet long and can give a shock of 200 volts. This is enough to stun the fishes on which it feeds, and one specimen was found with a 5lb. salmon in its stomach. The electric organs are contained in the wings of this ray.

There is only one group of marine bony fishes with electrical properties – the stargazers. In this group the electric organs are derived from the eye muscles. Electric-fishes are commoner in fresh waters than in the sea, but very weak electrical pulses – about four volts – have been detected coming from small organs in the tail of the common skate and some of its relatives. The function of these is not certain, but it has been suggested that they may be used to help a fish find members of the opposite sex.

TOUCH AND SOUND

Most fishes have what is called a lateral line, running along the side of the body. Under this line is a tube in the skin, and the lateral line is formed by a series of small pores from the tube opening onto the surface of the skin. The tube may send off small side branches, and almost always has branches running through many of the skull bones surrounding the brain. The tubes are filled with mucus, and in the mucus are small cells sensitive to vibrations and movement. This system is used for both hearing and, in a way, for touch.

When a fish moves it sets up a bow-wave in front of it. The cells in the lateral-line system can detect pressure changes in this bow-wave, and warn of an approaching fish, or warn the fish that it is approaching a rock. This gives the fish a sense of distant touch. Many deep-sea fishes rely heavily on this system to find their food and, at the same time, to avoid being eaten. In some fishes the pressure-sensitive cells may be found on the surface of the body.

Sound waves are carried under water as a series of pressure waves, and so the lateral-line system comes into use for hearing. The swim bladder also is used to pick up sound and in some fishes—the herring, for example—the swim bladder has little extensions running forward into the brain, where they lie close to the inner ear. Not only can fishes hear sound, but they can also make it. Rat-tails make drumming noises by vibrating the walls of the swim bladder. The gurnard makes a snoring noise, and the common name of the fish family, *Sciaenidae* (sigh-enid-e), is drum, because of their considerable vocal efforts. It is thought that the noise produced helps to keep shoals together at breeding time.

In some ways the bodies of fishes work rather like ours; they need oxygen, as we do, but they get it by exchanging, through the gills, the carbon dioxide in the blood for the oxygen in the water. Where there is light, they see. Smell is of great importance to fishes, as was mentioned when discussing shark attacks. As well as bumping into an object to touch it, they have a sense of distant touch. They can hear well—as many anglers know. In addition to all this, some fishes produce electricity, poison, and their own light.

A few species of fish are even able to leap out of the water and glide on wind currents to escape prey.

FLIGHT IN FISHES

Strictly speaking, the flying fishes of tropical seas do not fly, they glide. In the rivers of South America and Africa there are some fishes (freshwater hatchet fishes and the freshwater butterfly fish) that fly by actively flapping their pectoral fins which are provided with special muscles for that purpose. But the saltwater flying fishes, like the one shown on this page, just glide—but glide very efficiently. Their pectoral fins are very large and wing-like. Some species also have the pelvic fins enlarged. When flying fishes need to leave the water, they start swimming very quickly towards the surface. Near the surface the tail starts beating faster; then they make a sudden leap

Flying fish leaving the water

out of the water, often with the tail still touching the surface to give as much thrust as possible. The pectoral fins are extended and the fishes glide away. The fins are kept absolutely still while they are airborne. The flights are usually only just above the waves but a favourable draught can carry them up to 20 feet in the air and they have been known to land on the decks of ships. In good conditions a glide can be longer than a quarter of a mile. It is impossible for them to change direction while in the air but they can change direction by coming close to the surface of the water, letting the long lower lobe of the caudal fin trail in the water, and then giving it a sharp flip. This will not only change their course but also increase their speed.

Probably the main reason why flying fish take to the air is to evade being eaten by predators like the tunny. They also glide when frightened by a ship. Nonetheless there are instances when it seems that they leap out of the water just for fun.

REPRODUCTION IN FISHES

Most species of fish lay eggs, but a few species give birth to fully formed young. This is as true for the cartilaginous fishes — sharks and rays — as it is for the bony fishes. Firstly, we will consider the egg-laying fishes.

Those of you who like herrings will know that there are two sorts of roes, hard roes and soft roes. The roes are long, cream-coloured structures lying along the sides of the body cavity that contains the swim bladder and stomach. The hard roes are made up of tiny spherical objects, like very small balls. These are the eggs. So the hard roes come from the female herrings. The soft roes are smooth and are made up of millions of microscopic sperm. In fish, the male sperm is called milt. The egg cannot develop into a baby fish until it has been fertilized by milt. Generally, in most sea fishes, the female scatters her eggs into the water, and very soon afterwards the male sheds his milt over them to fertilize them.

Some fishes produce many millions of eggs, others only a few dozen. It is generally true that a species which produces many eggs has very small eggs, and the parents do not look after them. Fishes producing few eggs tend to have larger ones, and the parents are more likely to look after them.

A female herring, compared with some species, does not produce a great number of eggs. She will lay somewhere between 20,000 and 50,000 eggs in a series of sticky clumps, on the sea-bed. Once the eggs are laid and fertilized they are left to hatch or be eaten by the other inhabitants of the sea. One fish, called the ling (*Molva*), probably has the record for the greatest number of eggs laid. A large female ling that was caught, weighing 54lb., had nearly twenty-eight and a half million eggs in her ovaries (ovary is the technical word for the hard roe). A large cod will produce over 6 million eggs. The cod spawns over the continental shelf in cool waters. Once laid, the eggs float to the surface and drift in the currents. In cool waters they hatch in about twelve days. When laid, the eggs are less than $1\frac{1}{2}$ millimetres in diameter, and the newly hatched cod is about 4 millimetres long. While the eggs are floating in the sea, they are eagerly eaten by all sorts of animals. When the young cod hatches, it, in turn, starts eating the larvae and small eggs of other animals in the plankton. After some two to three months, the cod are about 1 inch long and they move inshore to start feeding off the bottom. Most of their adult life is spent near the bottom, sometimes at depths down to 1,000 feet.

FISH THAT CHANGE

The baby cod, or codling, is much like the adult, in the same way as a child is like an adult human. This, however, is not always the case. Some fishes undergo a great change between the larval and the adult states. All the flatfishes do this.

The adult flatfish, such as a plaice or a flounder, spends its life lying on its side on the bed of the sea. It has both eyes on the same side of its head, its mouth is twisted, and its body is fringed by the dorsal and anal fins. The pectoral and pelvic fins on the underside—usually called the blind side—are much smaller than their opposite numbers. The blind side is usually a pearly white, although occasionally pigment develops there. The upper side is dark, often with the ability to change colour. The plaice always lies on its left side, the turbot always on its right side. But newly hatched flatfishes have one eye on each side of the head and resemble normal fishes.

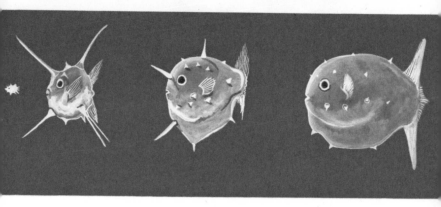

The oceanic sunfish changes its shape as it grows. The adult fish is shown on page 41

Flatfish eggs float at the surface of the sea. A turbot can lay up to 9 million, a flounder about 1 million, while a sole lays only about 500,000. Plaice eggs are much larger than many flatfish eggs, often nearly 2 millimetres in diameter. The eggs hatch out as normal larvae in a few days. When the larvae are about $\frac{1}{2}$ inch long, one eye moves round to the top of the head and then down the other side.

When the eye has moved down, the dorsal fin begins to grow forward. In the adult, it grows much farther forward than in other fishes. In some flatfishes the nostril on the blind side moves round too. While these changes are taking place, the

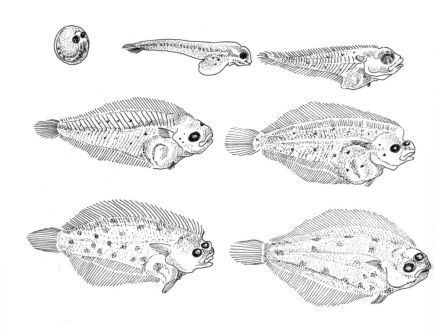

**The larval flatfish has its eyes
on opposite sides of its head.
As it grows it becomes flatter,
one eye changes sides, and finally
the fish lies on its side on the
bottom**

fish moves towards the sea-bed, and at the end of this change it lies on the sea-floor as a miniature version of the adult.

The ocean sunfish is another species with a strange life history. The adults are very large fishes, possibly as heavy as a ton in weight. They are flattened from side to side, have an odd tail fin, and swim in the surface waters by sculling movements of their oar-like dorsal and anal fins. The newly hatched larva is, like the plaice larva, quite normal. Soon it loses its tail fin and the body becomes covered with enormous spines, the shape begins to change, and at one stage the body is deeper than it is long. A new tail fin develops, but the muscles from the old tail fin are now attached to the lengthening dorsal and anal fins. From now on it slowly loses its spines and begins to resemble the adult. The spines are thought to be not only for protection, but to help it float since it has no swim bladder. The sunfish has a very small larva for such a big fish, and to reach its adult weight it must increase by some 60 million times.

Some fishes form shoals to breed. Others pair off, perhaps in shallow water or perhaps in the open sea. Salmon migrate from the sea into fresh waters to breed, while the eel moves from fresh waters into the sea to breed.

THE MYSTERY OF THE EELS

The life history of the eel has fascinated scientists since the days of the Greeks, but the full story was not known until this century. Eels are well known in European rivers and lakes, and it was known that at certain times of the year they would move towards the sea — overland if necessary. After that nothing more was known until small eels (elvers) about 6 inches long reappeared in the rivers. Aristotle knew that eels had never been found with eggs or sperm and thought that baby eels must arrive spontaneously "out of the bowels of the earth". The Roman, Pliny, thought that the eel was sexless, and that baby eels came from pieces of the parents' skin scraped off on rocks. Later theories included the suggestions that the hairs from the tail of a horse, or small beetles, gave rise to baby eels.

The discovery of the life history of the eel reads rather like a detective story. We will now consider an apparently unrelated event. Near the end of the eighteenth century a little fish called the Anglesey Morris (*Leptocephalus morrisii*) was discovered in English seas. This little fish was shaped like a willow leaf and was transparent. Similar-looking fishes had also been found in the Mediterranean. At the end of the last cen-

THE BREEDING CYCLE OF THE COMMON EEL
In the top left picture are a pair of adult European eels, which have grown up in a European river. Fully grown, they eventually set out across the Atlantic, swimming in the area which is marked in blue on the map. When they reach the striped area, in the region of the Sargasso Sea, they mate and breed. From the eggs laid in this part of the ocean, tiny leaf-like creatures hatch. These are the leptocephali, which are the larval form of the eel (top right). These tiny creatures then set out to swim back across the Atlantic, which is a journey taking some years, during which time they are growing. When at last they arrive in the estuaries of European rivers, they take the form of small eels, and are then known as elvers (bottom right)

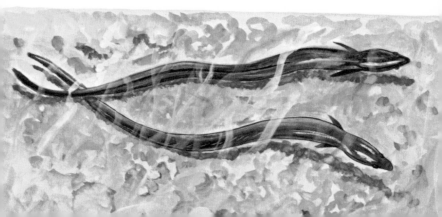

tury two Italian scientists kept these leptocephali (lep-toe-kef-ally) alive in an aquarium and after a while, to their amazement, they started shrinking, changed their shape, developed pigment in the skin and turned into baby eels. Now that a larval eel had been found, the next problem was to find where they bred. This was not discovered until about thirty years later. Dr Schmidt, a Danish zoologist, cruised over the Atlantic Ocean looking for leptocephali. He found the largest ones in the Mediterranean and on the European coast. As he travelled westwards, the leptocephali he caught were smaller. The smallest of all were caught in the Sargasso Sea off the American coast. Here, then, were the breeding-grounds of the eel. We now know that eels leave the rivers and ponds of Europe, go down to the sea and swim towards the Sargasso Sea 3-4,000 miles away. The eels spawn about 1,000 feet down. After spawning, the parents die. The eggs float for a while and then hatch. The tiny transparent larvae are carried back to Europe by the Gulf Stream, and it takes them three years to reach the coast. Once there, they change into elvers and make their way up rivers and into ponds.

THE FATHER-MOTHERS

The pipefishes and sea-horses (which are very closely related) do not undertake any long journey to breed, but they do have remarkable breeding habits. These fishes lay few eggs, and the father looks after them. In some pipefishes there is a simple groove on the belly of the male, and the female lays her eggs in this groove. In more advanced pipefishes the sides of the groove are raised to form a deep trough. In others, the sides of the trough are bent over to form a pouch. The end point is found in the sea-horse where the male has a pouch with a small slit-like opening just below his anal fin. When these fishes breed, the female injects her eggs into the pouch where they are fertilized. The inside of the pouch becomes spongy and full of blood vessels which are thought to nourish the eggs. The eggs hatch inside the pouch but the babies are not expelled at once. They stay in the pouch until their food supply (they are born with a yolk-sac) is finished. The male then rubs his pouch against a rock until the young are set free. In this way the father has almost become a "mother".

The common butterfish lays eggs in a clump and these are guarded by one of the parents until they hatch. The lumpsucker is a bulky fish found on European shores. The female lays about 100,000 eggs in rock cracks above the low-tide mark. The male guards the eggs for several weeks until they hatch. He moves them round to make sure that they get enough oxygen. The father lumpsucker is a devoted parent. Twice a day the eggs and himself are uncovered at low tide. Then sea-gulls try to eat the eggs and the father. When the eggs are covered the father defends them against any crabs or other fishes that try to eat them.

A fish called *Kurtus*, from the Indian Ocean, protects the eggs by hanging them on a hook that develops on the head of the male. Female sea catfishes of the family *Ariidae* (there is no general common name) lay very large eggs – up to $\frac{3}{4}$ inch in diameter. These are kept in the mouth of the male for up to a month until they hatch. During this time the male cannot feed.

MERMAID'S PURSES

All the fishes mentioned in detail so far are bony fishes and all have soft eggs. There is no shell as there is on a chicken's egg. Sharks and rays lay much larger eggs which have a leathery case. The egg-case of the skate is often washed up on the beach when the young has hatched, and it is known as a "mermaid's purse". Unlike the bony fishes, the sharks have internal fetilization. The pelvic fins of the male have two finger-like portions called claspers. These are used to transfer sperm to the eggs while they are inside the female and before they develop the leathery shell.

The shape of the eggs of different species of shark and ray is often distinctive. The egg of the lesser-spotted dogfish is

**The male sea horse (on the left)
has a pouch into which the female
lays her eggs, where they hatch**

much longer than it is wide, and each of the four corners has tendrils that catch on to seaweeds and hold the egg there until it hatches. The egg of the Port Jackson shark that lives in the Pacific Ocean is shaped like a large cone with a broad, flat spiral twisting round it.

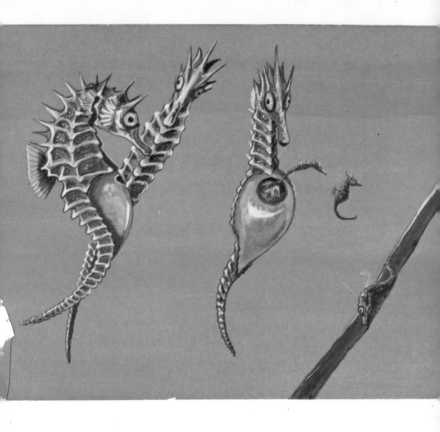

THE "LIVE-BIRTH" FISHES

One shark, the Greenland shark, was for a long time thought to lay eggs without a shell, which is an exception to the rule in sharks. This is now known not to be true. The Greenland shark, like the tope, spiny dogfish and many more, gives birth to fully developed young. The eggs hatch inside the mother. Stingrays give birth to fully formed young, and a special device has been developed to prevent the baby from stinging the mother. The spine of the baby stingray has a soft bulb of tissue covering the point, but once it has been born this is quickly lost.

**The leathery egg cases of a dogfish (right),
a Port Jackson shark (centre) and a skate
(left). The egg case of the skate is often
called a mermaid's purse**

The sawfishes also have young which hatch inside the
mother. The saw is soft at first and does not harden until after
birth. A female sawfish can have up to twenty-five young.
Some of the bony fishes give birth to fully developed young.
The eel-pout or viviparous blenny that was mentioned in
chapter two lives on the northern shores of Europe and can
have up to 300 babies. Fishes like the eel-pout and the surf-
perches, in which the eggs hatch inside the mother, must have
internal fertilization. Giving birth to fully developed young is
commoner in freshwater fishes than in sea fishes.

**The male sea catfish carries the eggs in
his mouth until they hatch**

FISH NESTS

Nest-building is also commoner among freshwater fishes.
One sea fish that does build a nest is the fifteen-spined stickleback. This species is much larger than the common three-
spined stickleback. It lives in the coastal waters of north-west
Europe and grows to about 8 inches long. In spring the male
makes a nest of strands of seaweed in seaweed beds below
the low-tide mark. The nest is not as neat as that of its three-
spined relative. The male persuades the females to lay their
eggs in this clump of seaweed strands. He then fertilizes the
eggs and stays on guard until the young hatch.

**The fifteen-spined stickleback and his
nest made of strands of seaweed**

**Opposite, a male lumpsucker
guarding the nest**

PARASITIC MALES

All the fishes so far described never have any great difficulty in finding a mate. They live in rich waters that support a lot of life, and will not have to travel very far before they find a mate. The life of deep-sea fishes is not so easy. As you already know, plants cannot live in the deep sea so fishes there are scarce. It has been suggested that for some species of fish there is only one individual per cubic mile of water. Because these fishes are not strong swimmers it would be difficult for them to find a mate. One group of fishes – the deep-sea angler-fishes – has gone to remarkable lengths to find an answer to this problem.

For many years all the deep-sea angler-fishes caught had rounded bodies, and very large teeth. They were little more than mouths and stomachs swimming around. As scientists developed better nets for catching smaller deep-sea fishes, some new, strange angler-fishes were caught. They were tiny fishes, lacking a lure and lacking the big teeth. Their teeth were rather like those of a rabbit—small, chisel-like teeth. It was difficult to understand how these fishes could eat in the deep sea. Eventually the answer was found. A normal deep-sea angler-fish was caught with some odd fleshy flaps on its body. These fleshy flaps were all that was left of the little chisel-toothed angler-fishes. We now know that the larger

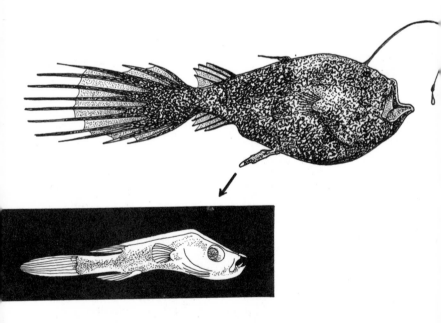

A female deep-sea angler-fish *(Ceratias holboeli)* with a parasitic male attached. The male is shown enlarged in the black panel

angler-fishes with the large teeth and the lures are females. The little ones are the males.

When adult only the females are known to feed. At the onset of maturity the male has to find a female in order to survive. When he meets one he bites into her skin and eventually the two bodies fuse. The male is no longer independent and is nourished by the female's blood stream. He loses his stomach, and the skin grows together between the two fishes so that the male cannot be separated. The female may be twenty times larger than the male, and there may be several parasitic males on one female. The male is now little more than a bag of milt, so that the female can have her eggs fertilized when they are ready, without having to worry about finding a male.

THE ROLE OF FISHES

In the previous chapters we have seen a little of what the sea is like: we have looked at the habits, shapes and structures of a very few examples of the many different sorts of fish in the sea. In this chapter we will briefly look at the problems of using the fishes in the sea – fishing and fish farming. We will also look at some of the exciting discoveries, and examine some of the mysteries of the sea.

Feeding the ever-increasing population of the world is becoming very difficult. The land is hard pressed to produce the necessary protein, and in some parts of the world is unable to do so. Therefore, people are looking more and more to the sea to provide the food.

Countries which have a long coastline near rich waters have been fishing for a long time. Britain has a long history of being a nation of fishermen, as have many European countries. Fishes were of great economic importance over 500 years ago. Consider the case of the herring. The herring is an ideal fish to catch. It swims near the surface of the sea in huge shoals, so it can easily be caught in drift nets. It is good to eat and can be treated in various ways to preserve it for export. The shoals may be several miles in length, and one drifter can catch perhaps 100,000 herring in one day.

Back in the middle of the fifteenth century there were great shoals of herring in the Baltic Sea. Many small towns became extremely rich on the profits from the herring fishery, and set themselves up as a series of small states called the Hanseatic League. In the middle of the fifteenth century, for no apparent reason, the herring left the Baltic Sea and the power of the Hanseatic states crumbled away. After this, the Dutch did most of the herring fishing. Later, when the Royal Navy beat the Dutch Navy and gave the British fishing boats freedom of the seas, the British became the major herring-fishing nation.

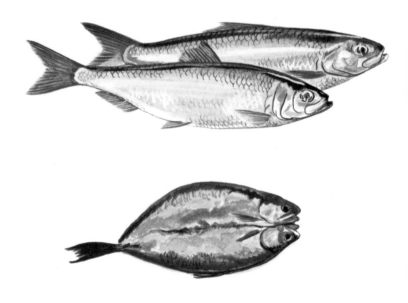

Fresh herrings and the result of curing them — a kipper

So you can see that the humble herring has had some effect upon European history and politics. In the last century much of the herring fishery was centred in the East Anglian ports of Yarmouth and Lowestoft. In recent times the herring shoals have decreased in size and no longer come within range of these ports, so their fortunes have declined.

It has been known for a long time that the herring shoals fluctuate. For many years the shoals will be large and appear regularly in the same area. Then, suddenly, they are gone. Scientists have tried to find out why. A few facts are known. It seems that in the Baltic Sea area there are regular changes in sea currents, and other changes occurring about every 1,800 years. This means that since the herrings were numerous in the Baltic in the Middle Ages, they were probably abundant about 600 B.C. If pollution permits, and the theories are right, there may be many shoals of herring in the Baltic again in about the thirty-second century.

WILL FISH BE USED UP?

The herring is an ideal fish to catch because of the ways in which it can be treated. Kippers are herrings that have been slit, soaked in brine — very strong salty water — and smoked. The kipper was probably developed in Newcastle on Tyne about 1843 by a man called John Woodger. Bloaters, red herrings and buckling are herrings that have been salted and smoked for different periods of time, giving different flavours.

Most of the fish species that are fished for commercially are shoaling fishes. The reason for this is obvious: keeping men and a boat at sea is expensive, so if the hold can be filled up quickly there is more profit for the fishermen. In the olden days the boats could not stay long at sea because there was no way of keeping the fish fresh. Nowadays the fishing boats can stay at sea for a month or more because they have refrigeration on the boats to keep the catch fresh.

From all this a danger arises, that of overfishing. Let us go back a hundred years or so. The boats could not travel far, nor

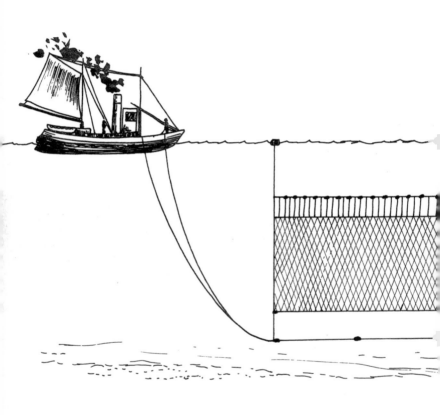

An old steam drifter and its nets, hanging vertically in the sea from a line of floats, fishing for herring

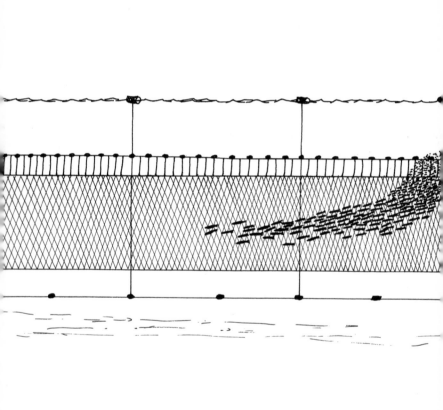

was there such a large population to feed. So although many herrings were caught, the great majority were untroubled by fishing. In the north European waters different populations of herring breed at different times of the year, so there is no time of the year when spawning is not taking place. Some herrings spawn in deep waters, and these would be safe from drift nets which can only catch the fishes in the top few feet of water. Overfishing occurs when more fish are caught in a year than hatch. This means that the numbers slowly go down. If an adult fish is ready to spawn, and is caught before it spawns, then all the young are lost from the future catches. The herring shoals that were too far from land to be caught a hundred years ago can now be caught easily. Trawl nets, pulled quickly through the water, can scoop up whole shoals. An echo sounder on the boat finds how deep the shoals are, and the boat is speeded up or slowed down until the net, which may be half a mile behind the boat, is at the same depth as the shoal and can make a large catch.

If fishes are caught on the breeding-grounds before breeding, the fish stocks fall because not enough young hatch to replace the adults caught. Many governments are aware of these problems, and various schemes have been tried to ensure a plentiful supply of fish.

We started off as hunters of fishes, but now perhaps we should try to be farmers of fishes.

Ignoring, for the moment, the effect of fishing, consider the number of eggs produced by, for example, the cod. A female cod can produce over 6 million eggs. If all the eggs hatched, and all the young lived to become adults from each pair of cod, there would be 6 million descendants; if each pair in the 6 million (i.e. 3 million pairs) produced the same number of eggs, it would not be long before there were more cod than sea. This just doesn't happen. You have seen in previous chapters how many sea creatures eat fish eggs and larvae. In this way the populations are kept within reasonable limits. It has been estimated that about one cod egg in every million gives rise to an adult fish.

The greatest natural loss of the fish stock is, therefore, at the egg and larval stages. If the eggs can be taken and hatched in safe waters, and the young allowed to grow until they are relatively safe from being eaten, then we have a possible way of solving the problems of overfishing.

In many fishery laboratories, at the moment, experiments are going on to find the best way of hatching and raising young fishes for eventual release in the sea. This is one of the ways that we may be able to keep people provided with fishes.

FISH FARMING

The problems of fish farming are, however, more complex than you may at first think. If, for example, country A spends a lot of money on hatching and raising the fishes, the government of A is not going to want the fishes to be caught by the trawlers of countries B and C after their release into the sea. If the journeys undertaken by the young fish were known and were always the same, doubtless the countries concerned could come to some financial agreement. Unfortunately the fishes do not behave like that. One vital aspect of fish farming is that it must be profitable – no country wants to lose money. Currently it seems that releasing young fish into the sea is uneconomical not only because they may swim away but also because too many are eaten. Sea lochs or closed-off bays of the sea have been suggested as possible rearing grounds for some species. What is being tried at the moment is rearing flatfish, usually the more expensive types, in large tanks under controlled conditions until they are large enough to eat. Not all species of fish can be reared in this fashion, but turbot do moderately well. It is quite possible that if you eat turbot in a few years' time, your fish may never have seen the sea.

A LIVING FOSSIL

It was a trawler fishing off the mouth of the Chalumna river on the east coast of South Africa that led to one of the most exciting and important zoological discoveries of recent times.

Just before Christmas 1938 a trawler docked at East London with a strange fish among its catch. This fish was blue, about 5 feet long and weighed over a hundredweight. It had heavy, rough scales, a large mouth with fang-like teeth, and fins with scaly lobes in the middle. The curator of the local museum, Miss Courtenay-Latimer, had never seen anything like it. The weather was hot and Miss Latimer had the problem of taking the fish to the museum and preserving it. She could not keep it for long and so a taxidermist stuffed the fish and threw away all the internal organs. Still not knowing what the fish was, Miss Latimer wrote to Professor J.L.B. Smith about it.

The letter arrived just after the New Year, and in Professor Smith's own words "its effects were those of an atomic blast". The fish was a coelacanth (seel-a-kanth). All coelacanths were thought to have died out in the Cretaceous period over 70 million years ago. The chance of finding one alive was about as slight as finding a dinosaur walking around.

Professor Smith hurried to East London to see the fish and found that, sadly, all the zoologically important internal organs, heart, stomach etc., had been thrown away. The coelacanth is a relative of the fishes that were our own ancestors, and it was important to see how the coelacanth's organs resembled our own.

If one fish was still alive, there must be more. Professor Smith had hundreds of notices printed, describing the fish, telling whom to contact if one was caught, and how to look after it until a scientist could arrive. Nothing further happened until Christmas Eve 1952, fourteen years later, almost to the day. On that day Professor Smith's dreams came true. He received a telegram saying that another coelacanth had been caught in the Comoro Islands, nearly 1,800 miles away from East London. It was the southern hemisphere's midsummer, and Christmas Eve. Professor Smith doubted if he could get there before the fish decayed. Eventually he asked the prime minister of South Africa to lend him an Air Force plane. There were many delays, because it is not easy to contact a prime minister over Christmas, especially about a dead fish. Eventually, after Christmas, Professor Smith flew up to the Comoro Islands, where he saw the second coelacanth and preserved it intact.

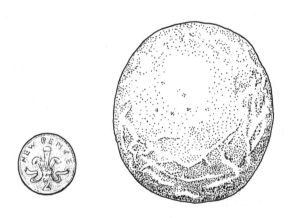

The egg of a coelacanth. It is probably the largest egg of any bony fish

Since the adventures in 1952 we now know that coelacanths are not uncommon round the Comoro Islands; the natives knew of them and had given them the name kombessa. They were caught by accident when fishing in deep water near rocks. Until the scientists of the world wanted coelacanths and offered to pay for them they were regarded as valueless by the natives. The flesh was not good to eat, but the scales were used to roughen the inner tubes of bicycle tyres when mending punctures. A recent, big scientific expedition went to the Indian Ocean equipped with tanks, pumps and cooling systems to try to keep a coelacanth alive. They wanted to know how its strange fins, which have in them the vestiges of the fore-runners of the bones in our own arms and legs, were used in swimming.

Coelacanths

They managed to keep one alive for a short while, but, unfortunately, the change in pressure (or temperature) from the deep water to the surface eventually killed the fish.

Over seventy have now been caught, and you can see specimens in some of the larger museums of the world. The most

A decomposing basking shark can look very different from the living animal. The gills fall away, leaving the spine exposed, and looking like a slender neck

recent one captured was a small female with eggs. Even the eggs are remarkable: this fish was under 3 feet long and had nineteen eggs—each about the size of a tennis ball, which probably makes them the largest of all fish eggs. You can see one in the Natural History Museum at South Kensington in London.

If a spectacular, odd, large, blue fish can remain hidden from science for 70 million years, can there be other exciting creatures in the sea? What, if they exist, are sea serpents?

MYSTERIES AND MONSTERS

Many early books and old legends tell of monsters in the sea. To a landlubber in the Middle Ages, a shark or a large skate would be a monster or an object of wonder. Sailors and fishermen would return from their voyages with tales of strange animals. Sometimes a half-rotted body, which had ceased to resemble the living animal, would be washed up. This would be misunderstood and tales would circulate of another sea monster.

Some of the monsters can be identified with real fishes. Many of the washed-up bodies that give rise to stories of sea serpents are the bodies of basking sharks. Basking sharks can grow to 30 feet long and when the corpse starts decomposing it soon loses its shark-like appearance. The gill slits in the basking shark are large, almost meeting each other at the top and bottom. This region soon rots and the gill area and lower jaw fall away. This exposes the front vertebrae and the small, shrunken cartilaginous skull. When in this condition it looks very like a long-necked monster with a small head.

Some of the common descriptions given to sea serpents seen swimming include "long body", "humps", and "red flowing mane". The oarfish *(Regalecus glesne)* has a ribbon-like body. The body is brilliantly silver, the dorsal fin is bright scarlet, and the first dozen or so rays very long. The long thin pelvic fins are bright red. It grows to over 20 feet in length, and the few that have been seen alive have been described as swimming on their sides at the surface of the sea. A fish swims by undulating its body in a series of waves. Do we not have here a fish that corresponds to some descriptions of sea serpents? Size and distance are very difficult to judge at sea because there are no landmarks to use. One of the difficulties with sea serpents

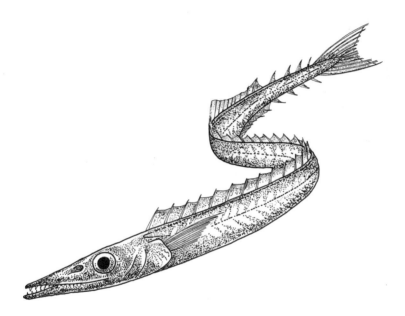

A snake mackerel

is that, with probably only one exception, no scientist has seen one. The corpses that have been examined are of known fishes. A sighting at sea by people who are not zoologists may lead to a wrong description of a known animal, and regrettably the sea serpent does not stay in the same place, so that it can be investigated.

Not all the sightings can be satisfactorily identified with known fishes. Two British naturalists, Mr Meade-Waldo and Mr Nicholl, were on board the yacht *Valhalla* off the coast of Brazil in December 1905 when they saw what appeared to be a large animal with a long neck (about 6 feet long) sticking out of the water, and a large dorsal fin behind it. What this was we do not know: were they mistaken or did they see a new species of animal?

There is a lot of sea, many parts of it rarely visited. Large ships make enough noise to frighten away any big animals. There are certainly some advantages to be gained by silence. The crew of the Kon-Tiki raft that floated across the Pacific Ocean found a live snake mackerel on the deck one night. The snake mackerel is a deep-sea fish that had never before been seen alive.

Let us finish this book by mentioning one further mystery. The larvae — leptocephali — of the common eel are just a few inches long, yet an adult common eel may weigh 10lb. The larvae of the conger eel are the same size and an adult conger may grow to 12 feet long and weigh over a hundredweight. The ship *Dana* caught a leptocephalus just over 6 feet long.

For some years after this discovery it was thought that this huge leptocephalus must grow into something even bigger — a gigantic eel that might possibly be the source of some of the stories about sea-serpents. The adult conger eel is many times larger than its leptocephalus. If the same were true for the Giant "Dana" leptocephalus, then it seemed possible that the adult eel may be over a hundred feet long.

Sadly, recent discoveries have discouraged this notion. The giant leptocephalus has been shown to be the larval form of a halosaur, a deep sea fish related to the eels. The

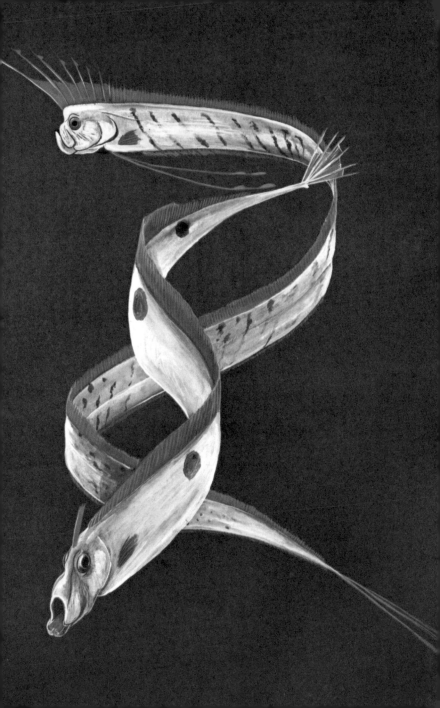

leptocephalus in this case is actually larger than the adult creature.

However, there are still unexplained sightings of strange objects at sea that will be subjects for speculation for years to come. Indeed, when one thinks about the very strange character of many sea-creatures that we do know about, one cannot help thinking that there may well be many others in the vast depths of the ocean that are even stranger, and that are totally unknown to us.

This odd looking fish, *Opisthoproctus*, (see page 47) has telescopic eyes which are directed upwards. This is one of the many odd creatures of the depths which are known to science

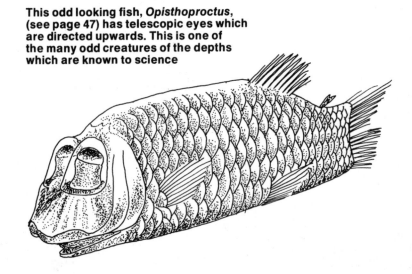

Above, the giant "Dana" leptocephalus, compared with that of a common eel. Below, the adult forms of the two larvae, halosaur and common eel

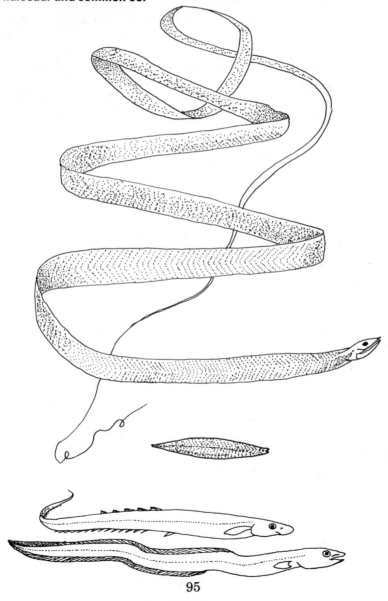